# FOCUS ON
# PARISH MUSIC

## Compiled by
## Kevin Mayhew

## With Liturgical and
## Scriptural Notes by
## Kevin Mayhew & Susan Sayers

Kevin Mayhew Publishers

This book gives only vocal editions of the various songs.
There is a separate accompaniment book which supplies
accompaniments for those pieces which need them.

First published in Great Britain in 1986 by
KEVIN MAYHEW LTD,
Rattlesden,
Bury St. Edmunds, Suffolk IP30 0SZ

ISBN 0 86209 082 2

We gratefully acknowledge the use of copyright
music throughout this book: copyright holders
are indicated alongside each piece.
The texts of the Gloria, Creed, Sanctus and
Lamb of God are copyright ICET.

Compilation © 1986 Kevin Mayhew Ltd

Cover design by Juliette Clarke
Music setting by Jeanne Fisher, London
Typesetting by David Holland Graphics, Colchester, Essex
Printed in Great Britain by Heronprint, London & Essex

# CONTENTS

# Foreword

The purpose of *Focus on Parish Music* is to provide a basic repertoire on which a parish can draw week after week. Its aim is modest: to be the bare bones of liturgical celebration on which more elaborate and adventurous music can be hung once the foundations are laid.

It is a book which sets out to help the community which has only the most modest musical resources at its disposal, though I hope more expert parishes will also find in it much useful material.

Besides making available simple and attractive music for the Penitential Rite, Gloria, Sanctus and Agnus Dei, the book also concentrates on the important but neglected area of acclamation. It includes Gospel Acclamations, Memorial Acclamations and Great Amens which are easy to sing and immediate in effect.

The core of the book is a set of Responsorial Psalms suitable for use throughout the year. These are the alternative Psalms recommended in the Lectionary as particularly suitable for singing, and they are presented here with melodies which choirs and congregations will sing with pleasure.

Much of the music is *responsorial* in character: a cantor or choir sings out the tune and everyone repeats it. Once a congregation has got hold of this simple principle it is relatively easy to introduce a lot of new music.

Each phrase to be sung and repeated ends with a double bar line (‖). Thus, in *Penitential Rite* 1 on page 7, the cantor or choir sings 'Lord, have mercy' and everyone repeats it; then similarly with 'Christ, have mercy' and the final 'Lord, have mercy'.

This method of helping the people – giving them confidence to sing out – can be used just as effectively in the longer pieces. In *Gloria* 2 on page 10, for example, the cantor or choir may sing the Refrain at the beginning to remind the people of the melody until such time as they are sure of it. The same principle applies to the *Responsorial Psalms* and, of course, to the shorter pieces throughout the book.

*Focus on Parish Music* has its roots in a personal need which I know is shared by many others who are active in the music ministry in their community.

For some years I have been involved in the liturgical music at St Joseph's, Hadleigh, Suffolk. We are a small community and our music is led by an enthusiastic group of singers and instrumentalists, encouraged by a willing congregation. None of us is musically outstanding, though by dint of hard work we are competent and produce a pleasing sound; and, because we try to understand what the liturgy is saying to our community, our celebration works as an act of praise more often than not.

Much of the music in *Focus on Parish Music* was written for and tried out by the choir and congregation of St Joseph's. To them and to the composers and authors who have contributed to the book: thank you.

If you recognise yourself and your community in this description I hope you will also find something here for your needs.

Kevin Mayhew

# Introductory Rites

## PENITENTIAL RITE

The Penitential Rite is part of the Introductory Rites of the Mass whose purpose is to help us become a worshipping community. This is a time for warmth, mutual acceptance, concern and regard, a time when we prepare to listen to God's Word and celebrate the Eucharist.

After a joyful processional song the celebrant invites us to acknowledge our sinfulness before our forgiving Lord. Our response is not only a plea for forgiveness but also an acknowledgement of the saving presence of the risen Christ in our midst.

## 1 PENITENTIAL RITE 1
### Music by Estelle White

▶ A very simple setting, each section best sung first by the Cantor (or choir) and repeated by everyone.

Lord, have mer-cy. Christ, have mer-cy. Lord, have mer-cy.

## 2 PENITENTIAL RITE 2
### Music by Kevin Mayhew

▶ Another 'immediate' setting: Cantor first, then everyone.

Lord, have mer – cy. Christ, have mer – cy. Lord, have mer – cy.

## 3 PENITENTIAL RITE 3
### Music by Kevin Mayhew

▶ Just a little more elaborate; sing it smoothly!

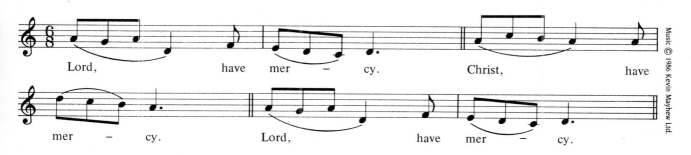

Lord, have mer – cy. Christ, have mer – cy. Lord, have mer – cy.

## 4 PENITENTIAL RITE 4
### Music by Estelle White

▶ Although this is longer it is just as easy to sing: the people's part still repeats what the Cantor has sung.

## 5 PENITENTIAL RITE 5
### Music by Martin Morran

▶ Perhaps a setting for the more 'special' occasion!

## GLORIA

This hymn of praise begins with the words heard by the shepherds when Jesus was born (*Luke* 2:14). Although it is not known when or by whom the hymn was composed, it was in use as part of morning prayer in the 4th century.

In the Gloria we worship God, praise and thank him through Jesus Christ who takes away our sins and presents our prayer to the Father who alone is holy and whose life we are called to share.

# 6 GLORIA 1
## Music by Julian Wiener

▶ Keep a good, steady one-in-a-bar beat going for this. It will help the people if the Cantor sings the Refrain at the very beginning, just to remind them.

*Refrain: All*

Glo-ry, glo-ry, glo-ry, glo-ry to God in the high — est;
glo-ry, glo-ry, glo-ry, and peace to his peo-ple on earth.

*Music © 1986 Kevin Mayhew Ltd.*

*Cantor*

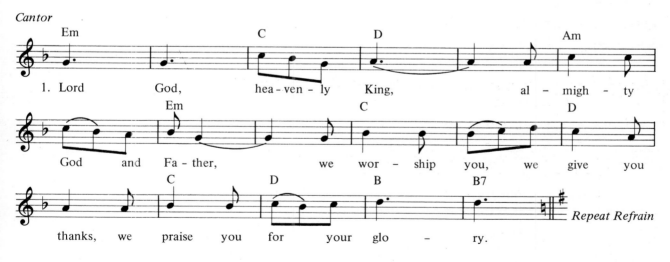

1. Lord God, hea-ven-ly King, al-migh-ty God and Fa-ther, we wor-ship you, we give you thanks, we praise you for your glo — ry.

*Repeat Refrain*

*Cantor*

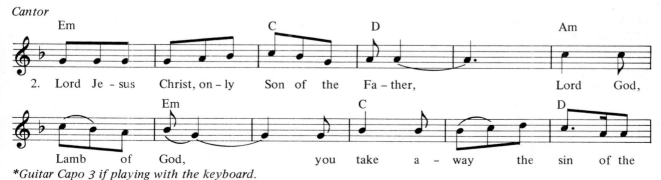

2. Lord Je-sus Christ, on-ly Son of the Fa-ther, Lord God, Lamb of God, you take a-way the sin of the

*Guitar Capo 3 if playing with the keyboard.

world:   have   mer - cy   on   us;                                    *Repeat Refrain*

*Cantor*

3. you   are   sea - ted   at   the   right   hand   of   the   Fa - ther:                   re -

- ceive   our   pray'r.   For   you   a - lone   are   the   Ho - ly

One,   you   a - lone   are   the   Lord,                                *Repeat Refrain*

*Cantor*

4. you   a - lone   are   the   Most   High,

Je - sus   Christ,   with   the   Ho - ly   Spi -

- rit,   in   the   glo - ry   of   God   the   Fa - ther.                 *Repeat Refrain*

---

# 7   GLORIA 2
## Music by Kevin Mayhew

▶ The Refrain should be sung with verve, but take
care that the verses do not become disjointed:
sing them smoothly, and not too fast.

*Refrain: All*

Glo-ry   be   to   God on   high,   peace on   earth   to   all his   friends.   Glo-ry

be   to   God on   high,   peace on   earth   to   all   his   friends.                 *Fine*

## 8  GLORIA 3
### Words and Music by
### Noel Donnelly

▶ This setting could act as an alternative to the
'Peruvian' Gloria!

*Refrain: All*

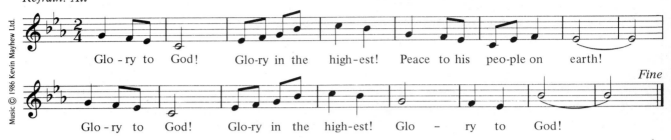

Glo-ry to God! Glo-ry in the high-est! Peace to his peo-ple on earth!

*Fine*

Glo-ry to God! Glo-ry in the high-est! Glo - ry to God!

*Cantor*

Glo-ry to God the Fa - ther! Glo-ry to God the Son!

Glo-ry to God the Spi-rit! Praise to the God of love!

*Repeat Refrain*

# Liturgy of the Word

## RESPONSORIAL PSALM

The psalm follows the first reading and should enable us to meditate on the Word of God. Clearly, a congregation reciting a response after a verse spoken by a Reader is not what those who revised the liturgy had in mind! They expected the psalm to be sung!

However, most communities have discovered two difficulties in achieving this: first, the psalm changes every day and second, every verse has a different rhythm, usually necessitating a chant-like setting.

The Lectionary solves the first problem by stating: '... to make it easier for the people to sing the Responsorial Psalm, certain *Common Texts* are given ... These may be substituted for the text given in the Lectionary for a particular day ...'

We hope we have solved the second problem by providing texts which fall into a regular rhythmic pattern, thus enabling them to be set to the kind of music more familiar to the Catholic ear.

## 9 ADVENT 1: Psalm 24
### Versified and set to music by Susan Sayers

*This psalm enables us to join the psalmist in admitting our waywardness and acknowledging that in our weakness, God is our only sure and trustworthy guide. It is a frank admission of our need for constant redirection.*

▶ Keep this one moving.

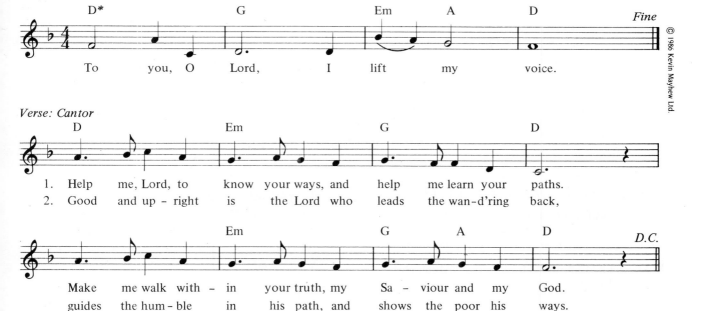

*Response: All*

To you, O Lord, I lift my voice.

*Verse: Cantor*

1. Help me, Lord, to know your ways, and help me learn your paths.
2. Good and up-right is the Lord who leads the wan-d'ring back,

Make me walk with-in your truth, my Sa-viour and my God.
guides the hum-ble in his path, and shows the poor his ways.

\* *Guitar Capo 3 if playing with the keyboard.*

3. Faithfulness and love abound
   for all who keep his word;
   those who love him have a friend
   whose promise is made clear.

## 10 ADVENT 2: Psalm 84
Versified by Susan Sayers
Music by Gerry Fitzpatrick

▶ A good tune; enjoy it especially in the last eight
bars of the verse!

*This is the second part of the psalm which shows
first-hand experience of God's willingness to forgive
and restore, time after time. Now such knowledge is
projected forward to an age when the joyous harmony
of God's order and peace pervade the world.*

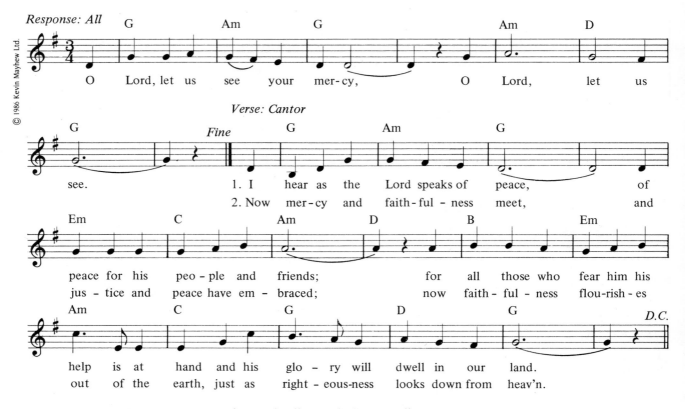

3. The Lord will provide for us well,
   our earth shall yield plentiful fruit,
   and righteousness shall be the standard of God,
   while behind him shall peacefulness tread.

## 11 CHRISTMAS: Psalm 97
Versified and set to music
by Susan Sayers

▶ Keep a good steady one-in-a-bar rhythm, and
sing with joy.

*The psalmist looks ahead to the time when God's
salvation will be known to all the nations, having
begun with the house of Israel. Their privileged
position, as 'enablers' of God's will, is a great reason
for rejoicing.*

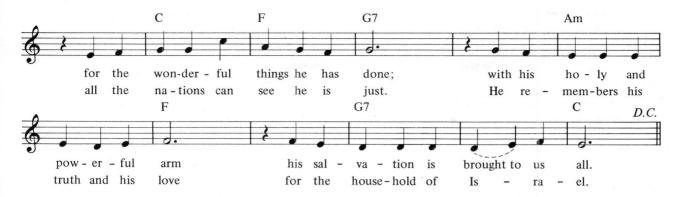

for the | won-der-ful | things he has | done; | with his | ho-ly and
all the | na-tions can | see he is | just. | He re-mem-bers his

pow-er-ful | arm | his sal-va-tion is | brought to us | all.
truth and his | love | for the house-hold of | Is-ra-el.

*D.C.*

3. All the ends of the earth have now seen
   the salvation brought to us by God.
   Shout aloud to the Lord, all the earth,
   as you ring out your joy in his praise.

4. O sing psalms to the Lord with the harp,
   and with music sing praise to the Lord;
   with the trumpet, and blasts of the horn,
   we acknowledge the Lord who is King.

## 12 LENT 1: Psalm 50
### Versified and set to music by Susan Sayers

▶ Keep the tune moving: it reflects the words very well.

*Linked with David and his affair with Bathsheba, this poignant psalm makes it clear that whatever evil has been committed, complete repentance will be followed by God's forgiveness. The words evocatively express man's awareness of sin and his longing for reconciliation.*

*Response: All*

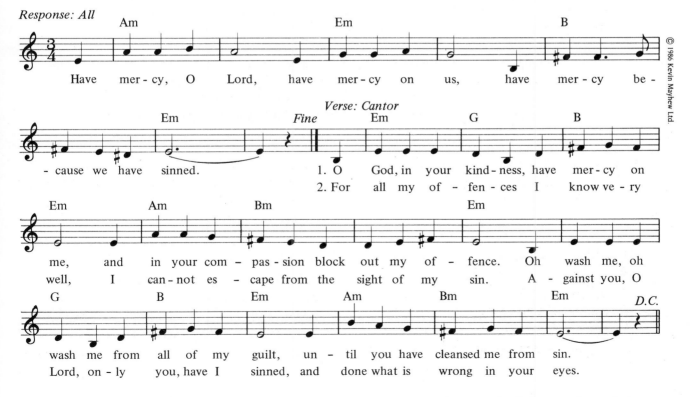

Have mer-cy, O Lord, have mer-cy on us, have mer-cy be-

*Verse: Cantor*

-cause we have sinned.

1. O God, in your kind-ness, have mer-cy on
2. For all my of-fen-ces I know ve-ry

me, and in your com-pas-sion block out my of-fence. Oh wash me, oh
well, I can-not es-cape from the sight of my sin. A-gainst you, O

wash me from all of my guilt, un-til you have cleansed me from sin.
Lord, on-ly you, have I sinned, and done what is wrong in your eyes.

*D.C.*

3. A pure heart create in your servant, O Lord;
   a steadfast and trustworthy spirit in me.
   O cast me not out from your presence, I pray,
   and take not your Spirit from me.

4. Restore to me, Lord, all the joy of your help;
   sustain me with fervour, sustain me with zeal.
   Then open my lips and my mouth shall declare
   the praise of my Lord and my God.

## 13 LENT 2: Psalm 90
### Versified by Susan Sayers
### Music by Julian Wiener

▶ Keep the Response broad and slow: remember that there are quite a number of quick notes in the verse.

*Coming after psalms 88 and 89, which suggest God rejecting and abandoning his people, as they have rejected his Law, this psalm asserts with confidence that, ultimately, he will protect and preserve them from danger. He loves his children intimately, knowing each one by name.*

3. They are there to support you, and will bear you up
   if you should trip or stumble;
   you'll tread on the adder and the lion,
   and trample the serpent underfoot.

4. When you hold to me lovingly I set you free,
   I rescue those who know me;
   whenever you call I answer you,
   I save you and show you my respect.

## 14 LENT 3: Psalm 129
### Versified and set to music
### by Susan Sayers

▶ Sing gently and meditatively.

*Suitable for both an individual and a community, this psalm emphasises that man has no hope for survival apart from God's grace. It is an admission of our weakness and our need for his intervention.*

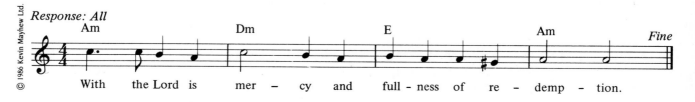

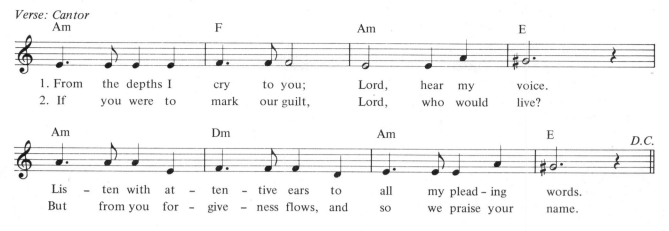

*Verse: Cantor*

1. From the depths I cry to you; Lord, hear my voice.
2. If you were to mark our guilt, Lord, who would live?

Lis - ten with at - ten - tive ears to all my plead - ing words.
But from you for - give - ness flows, and so we praise your name.

3. For my soul awaits the Lord;
in him I trust.
Longingly I wait for him
as watchmen wait for dawn.

4. Since the Lord, the merciful,
comes to redeem,
Israel will be redeemed
from all her sin and shame.

# 15 EASTER 1: Psalm 117
### Versified by James Quinn
### Music by Gerry Fitzpatrick

▶ This setting is a really good sing. Perhaps the Cantor could sing the first part of the line in the verse, the rest of the choir joining in with 'for his love knows no end,' and so on.

*Sung during the entry procession to the temple at important festivals, this is a communal act of praise and thanks. Christians see special significance in the rejected stone which becomes the 'corner stone', the keystone, or foundation, as Jesus fulfilled this role.*

Words © James Quinn S. J. Reprinted by permission of Geoffrey Chapman a division of Cassell Publishers Limited, London.

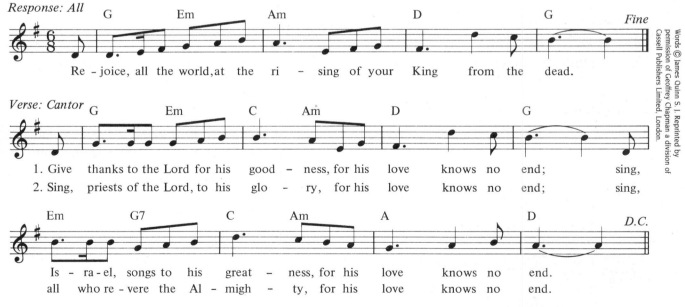

*Response: All*

Re - joice, all the world, at the ri - sing of your King from the dead.

*Verse: Cantor*

1. Give thanks to the Lord for his good - ness, for his love knows no end; sing,
2. Sing, priests of the Lord, to his glo - ry, for his love knows no end; sing,

Is - ra - el, songs to his great - ness, for his love knows no end.
all who re - vere the Al - migh - ty, for his love knows no end.

3. The Lord with his right hand has triumphed:
he has raised me to life;
the Lord with his right hand has triumphed:
I will live in his praise.

4. The stone that was spurned for the building
is its keystone of strength;
this work is the work of God's glory,
and a marvel to all.

5. This day is the day of his making,
day of gladness and joy;
give thanks to the Lord for his goodness,
for his love knows no end.

## 16 EASTER 2: Psalm 65
### Versified by Susan Sayers
### Music by Martin Morran

▶ A good, strong tune. Resist the temptation to swoop, though!

*Here the whole community is invited to share the exhuberant joy of an individual's witness during an offering of thanksgiving; in fact, the whole of God's created world is encouraged to join in his act of praise.*

*Response: All*

Cry out with joy to God, all the earth, al - le - lu - ia.

*Verse: Cantor*

1. O cry out with joy, all the earth, to your God,
2. 'Be - fore you, in awe, bows the whole of the earth,

sing to his hon - oured and glo - ri - ous name.
ev' - ry - one sing - ing and prais - ing your name!'

Give him the rev' - rance and praise he is due, and
Come, and see all that our God has per - formed — his

say to him 'Fa - ther, how great are your works.'
deal - ings are won - d'rous, a - stound-ing to see.

3. When God made a path through the midst of the sea
they crossed the river and kept their feet dry.
We shall rejoice, then, because of his love;
he rules us for ever with power and might.

4. Let all who fear God, come and listen to me.
Hear what the Lord has accomplished for me:
praise be to God who has not shunned my prayer;
his steadfast affection is never withheld.

## 17 PENTECOST: Psalm 103
### Versified and set to music by Aniceto Nazareth

▶ Sing with life: the verse goes beautifully into the Response.

*Here the psalmist reflects on the dependence of all creatures on God for every need, and on God's ordered provision for those he has made. Having recognised this dependence, the psalmist reaffirms his commitment to living in God's way.*

*Response: All*

Send forth your Spi - rit, O Lord, that the face of the earth be re - newed.

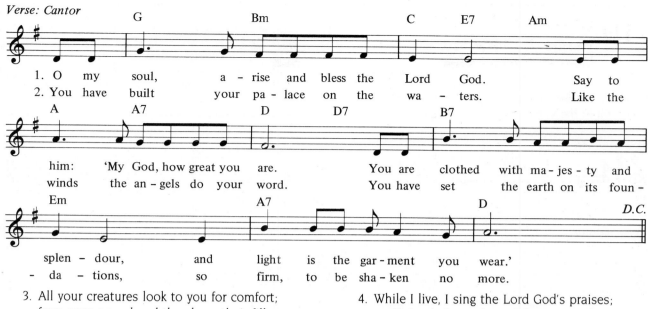

*Verse: Cantor*

1. O my soul, a – rise and bless the Lord God. Say to
2. You have built your pa – lace on the wa – ters. Like the

him: 'My God, how great you are. You are clothed with ma – jes – ty and
winds the an – gels do your word. You have set the earth on its foun –

splen – dour, and light is the gar – ment you wear.'
– da – tions, so firm, to be sha – ken no more.

3. All your creatures look to you for comfort;
   from your open hand they have their fill.
   You send forth your Spirit and revive them,
   the face of the earth you renew.

4. While I live, I sing the Lord God's praises;
   I will thank the author of these marvels.
   Praise to God, the Father, Son and Spirit,
   both now and for ever. Amen.

# 18 ORDINARY TIME 1: Psalm 18
## Versified by Susan Sayers
## Music by Estelle White

*This section of the psalm celebrates God's Law, with its great power for good. The Law is seen as a revelation of God himself and his will, so that as man follows it he will be led to a deeper relationship with his creator.*

▶ Try to sing the long phrases in the verse in one breath: it will enhance the meaning of the words.

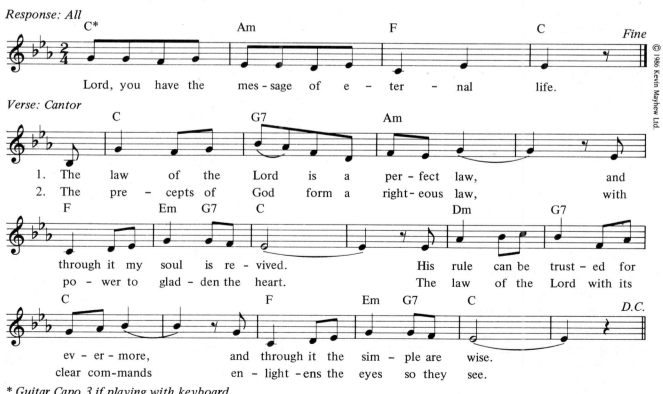

*Response: All*

Lord, you have the mes – sage of e – ter – nal life.

*Verse: Cantor*

1. The law of the Lord is a per – fect law, and
2. The pre – cepts of God form a right – eous law, with

through it my soul is re – vived. His rule can be trust – ed for
po – wer to glad – den the heart. The law of the Lord with its

ev – er – more, and through it the sim – ple are wise.
clear com – mands en – light – ens the eyes so they see.

*\* Guitar Capo 3 if playing with keyboard.*

3. The fear of the Lord is a holy fear,
   abiding without any end.
   Decrees of the Lord are decrees of truth,
   and all of his statutes are just.

4. His law is desired more than costly gold,
   more precious than purest of gold;
   far sweeter than honey are all his laws,
   than sweet honey fresh from the comb.

## 19 ORDINARY TIME 2: Psalm 26
### Versified by Susan Sayers
### Music by Martin Morran

*This psalm may have been used in a night vigil during which the psalmist concentrates his mind and heart on trusting God, searching and waiting for him patiently. Even through times of personal distress he is confident that God will help him.*

▶ A broad melody which needs plenty of breath control in the verse.

*Response: All* ... *Fine*

The Lord is my light and my help.

*Verse: Cantor*

1. The Lord is my light and my help; of whom, then, shall
2. One thing I have asked of the Lord — to live in his

I be a-fraid? The Lord is the strength in my
house all my days; to gaze on the beau-ty of

*D.C.*

life; be-fore whom shall I need to cow-er?
God, to seek out his will in his tem-ple.

3. His goodness shall surely be shown,
revealed to me while I still live;
stand firm and the Lord will give strength;
O hope in the Lord who supports you.

## 20 ORDINARY TIME 3: Psalm 33
### Versified by James Quinn
### Music by Noel Donnelly

*This is an 'alphabet' psalm, each verse beginning in the Hebrew original with a letter of the alphabet, possibly to emphasise total commitment, and reverence for the language of God's Law. Linked with the time, at the Philistine palace, David pretended to be mad in order to escape death, this psalm joyfully proclaims God's help in times of danger or anxiety.*

▶ This lovely setting will repay some special care and attention; take it steadily.

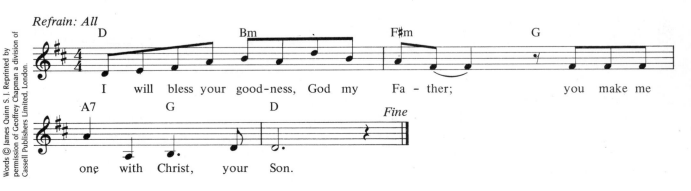

*Refrain: All*

I will bless your good-ness, God my Fa-ther; you make me

*Fine*

one with Christ, your Son.

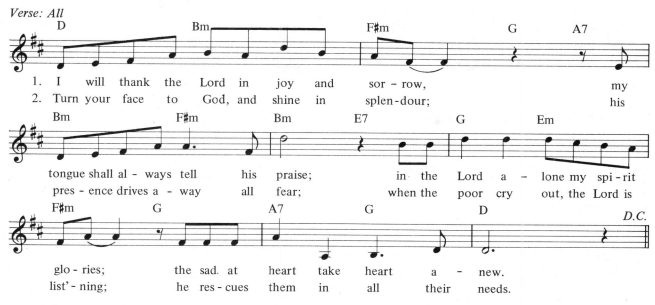

*Verse: All*

1. I will thank the Lord in joy and sor - row, my
2. Turn your face to God, and shine in splen-dour; his

tongue shall al - ways tell his praise; in the Lord a - lone my spi - rit
pres - ence drives a - way all fear; when the poor cry out, the Lord is

glo - ries; the sad. at heart take heart a - new.
list' - ning; he res - cues them in all their needs.

3. Like an army, angels gather round us,
   to shelter those who fear his name.
   Taste and see how gracious is his goodness!
   How happy those who trust in God!

4. Keep your tongue from speaking any evil,
   your lips from any lying word;
   turn aside from wrong to ways of goodness,
   and always seek the paths of peace.

5. God will set his face against the wicked;
   their name will fade beyond recall;
   he will turn to hear his faithful servants,
   and give them what they ask in love.

6. When they pray, the Lord will hear them calling,
   and prove himself their friend in need;
   he is near to heal the broken-hearted,
   the downcast he uplifts in love.

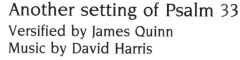

## Another setting of Psalm 33
### Versified by James Quinn
### Music by David Harris

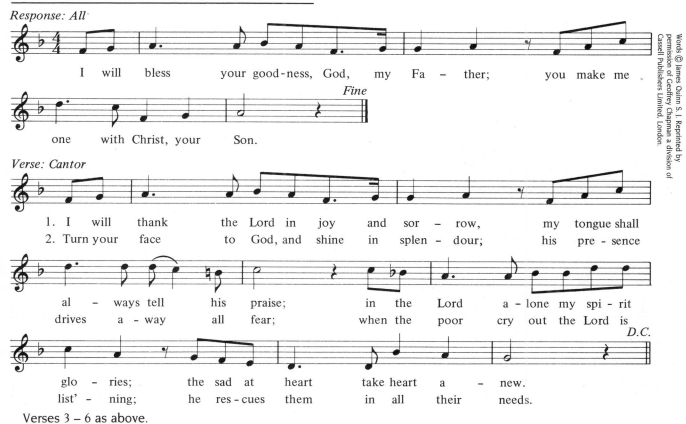

*Response: All*

I will bless your good-ness, God, my Fa - ther; you make me

*Fine*

one with Christ, your Son.

*Verse: Cantor*

1. I will thank the Lord in joy and sor - row, my tongue shall
2. Turn your face to God, and shine in splen - dour; his pre - sence

al - ways tell his praise; in the Lord a - lone my spi - rit
drives a - way all fear; when the poor cry out the Lord is

glo - ries; the sad at heart take heart a - new.
list' - ning; he res - cues them in all their needs.

Verses 3 – 6 as above.

Words © James Quinn S.J. Reprinted by permission of Geoffrey Chapman a division of Cassell Publishers Limited, London.

## 21 ORDINARY TIME 4: Psalm 62
### Versified and set to music by Kevin Mayhew

*This psalm would have been written before the Babylonian exile, and may have been used at a vigil during a time of hardship, such as when David had fled into the loneliness of the wilderness. Again, there is the trust which recognises God's constant presence and protection, even when times are bad.*

▶ Take a two-in-a-bar rhythm and sing with confidence.

*Response: All*

You are my God, the God of my life, my soul is thirst-ing for you.

*Verse: Cantor*

1. You are my God, it is you that I seek,
2. Day af-ter day I will watch in your house:

I am thirst-ing for you; just as a land that is
you are glo-ry and pow'r; bet-ter than life is your

wea-ry and parched, longs my bod-y for you.
love for your child, I shall sing to your praise.

3. All my life long I will bless you, my God,
   lift my hands in your name;
   richly my soul will be feasted with love,
   I shall praise you with joy.

4. I will remember you, Lord, when I sleep,
   I will watch through the night;
   you are my help and with you I am safe
   in the shade of your wing.

## 22 ORDINARY TIME 5: Psalm 94
### Versified by Susan Sayers
### Music by Julian Wiener

*This is a call to all the people of God to join in worship. Israel sees God not only as maker of the world, but also as her shepherd and special guide. But the people of Israel must be open to their God — otherwise they will find their false worship rejected.*

▶ Sing this with a fairly snappy rhythm.

*Response: All*

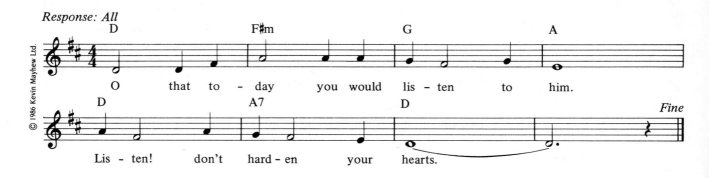

O that to-day you would lis-ten to him.

Lis-ten! don't hard-en your hearts.

*Verse: Cantor*

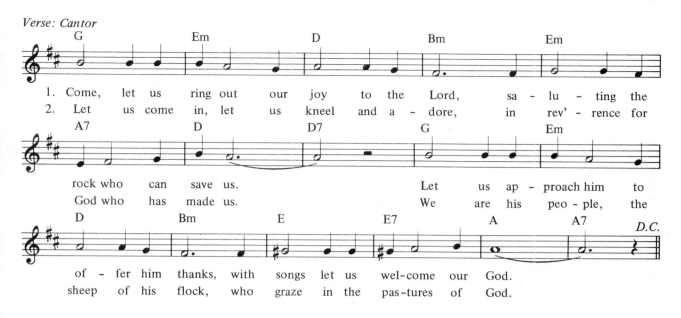

1. Come, let us ring out our joy to the Lord, sa - lu - ting the
2. Let us come in, let us kneel and a - dore, in rev' - rence for

rock who can save us. Let us ap - proach him to
God who has made us. We are his peo - ple, the

of - fer him thanks, with songs let us wel-come our God.
sheep of his flock, who graze in the pas-tures of God.

3. Out in the desert they hardened their hearts,
   at Massah they tested their Saviour;
   O that today you would listen to him,
   and open your hearts to his love.

## Another setting of Psalm 94

Versified by Susan Sayers
Music by Dom Gregory Murray

▶ Keep the Response broad and slow: remember
that there are a lot of quick notes in the verse.

*Response: All*

O that to - day you would lis - ten to him.

*Fine*

Lis - ten! don't hard - en your hearts.

*Verse: Cantor*

1. Come, let us ring out our joy to the Lord, sa - lu - ting the rock who can save us.
2. Let us come in, and in re - ver-ence bow to kneel be -fore God who has made us.

*D.C.*

Let us ap-proach him to of - fer him thanks, with songs let us wel- come the Lord.
We are his peo - ple, the sheep of his flock, a flock in the pas-tures of God.

See above for verse 3.

## 23 ORDINARY TIME 6: Psalm 99
Versified by Susan Sayers
Music by Estelle White

*This was one of the psalms sung by the people as they entered the temple at Jerusalem. It is an acclamation of trust in the bond which links God with his children in unswerving loyalty and love.*

▶ Sing with movement and life!

3. Oh, how great and how good is the Lord,
   loving us for ever;
   rich in mercy and faithfulness,
   true throughout ev'ry age.

## 24 ORDINARY TIME 7: Psalm 102
Versified by Susan Sayers
Music by Kevin Mayhew

*This psalm probably dates from after the exile in Babylon. It celebrates the constant love and care God shows in his dealings with man, based on the many experiences of Israel's history.*

▶ Try to phrase the music in the verse to reflect the sense of the words.

* Guitar Capo 3 if playing with keyboard.

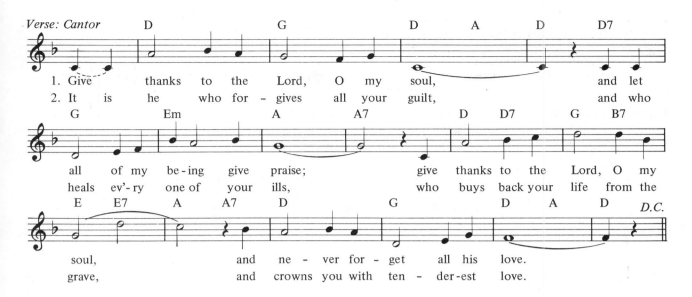

**Verse: Cantor**

1. Give thanks to the Lord, O my soul, and let
2. It is he who for-gives all your guilt, and who

all of my be-ing give praise; give thanks to the Lord, O my
heals ev'-ry one of your ills, who buys back your life from the

soul, and ne-ver for-get all his love.
grave, and crowns you with ten-der-est love.

3. The Lord is compassion and love,
   rich in mercy and slow to condemn.
   The punishment that we deserve,
   in merciful love he forgoes.

4. As far as the East is from West
   just as far he removes us from sin.
   As fathers are tender to sons
   so tender is God to his own.

## Another setting of Psalm 102
**Versified by Susan Sayers**
**Music by Noel Donnelly**

▶ A more straightforward setting with a jaunty tune.

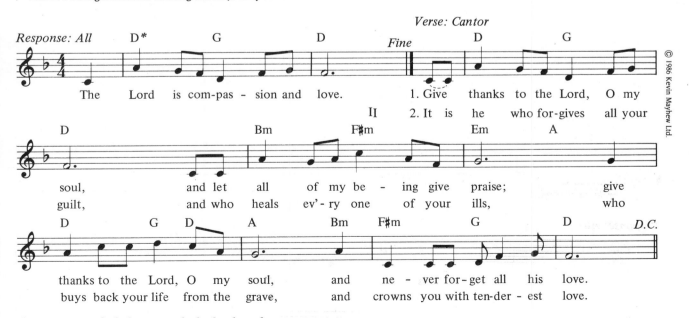

**Response: All**

The Lord is com-pas-sion and love. *Fine*

**Verse: Cantor**

1. Give thanks to the Lord, O my
2. It is he who for-gives all your

soul, and let all of my be-ing give praise; give
guilt, and who heals ev'-ry one of your ills, who

thanks to the Lord, O my soul, and ne-ver for-get all his love.
buys back your life from the grave, and crowns you with ten-der-est love.

*\* Guitar Capo 3 if playing with the keyboard.*

See above for verses 3 and 4.

## 25 ORDINARY TIME 8: Psalm 144
Versified by Susan Sayers
Music by Gerry Fitzpatrick

*This glorious song of praise is one of the 'acrostic' or alphabet psalms, with each verse starting with a letter of the Hebrew alphabet. The encompassing of language reflects the encompassing of all creation by God's love, and his worthiness to receive endless praise.*

▶ You will need to take care with the pitch of the notes in the first bar of the verse. Otherwise, sing it with verve.

*Response: All*

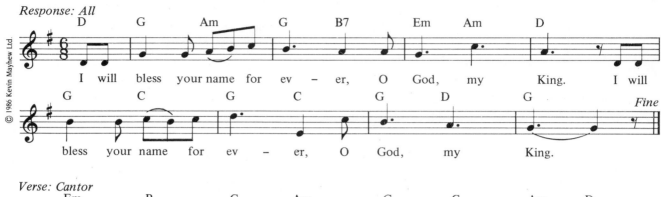

I will bless your name for ev – er, O God, my King. I will
bless your name for ev – er, O God, my King. *Fine*

*Verse: Cantor*

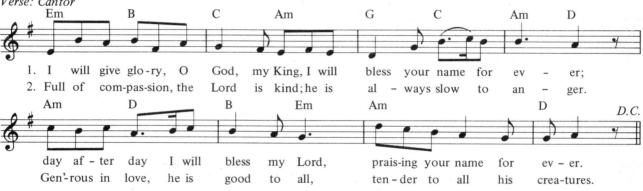

1. I will give glo-ry, O God, my King, I will bless your name for ev – er;
2. Full of com-pas-sion, the Lord is kind; he is al – ways slow to an – ger.

day af – ter day I will bless my Lord, prais-ing your name for ev – er.
Gen'-rous in love, he is good to all, ten – der to all his crea-tures.

3. All of creation shall thank you, Lord,
   and your faithful servants bless you;
   they shall proclaim all your splendid acts,
   telling of all your greatness.

4. Faithful is God in the words he speaks;
   he is love in all his actions.
   He will support all who slide and fall,
   comfort the sad and weary.

## 26 ORDINARY TIME 9: Psalm 121
Versified and set to music
by Susan Sayers

*Pilgrims would have sung this psalm as they approached Jerusalem, during the Feast of Tabernacles, for instance. But Jerusalem is intended also as a symbol of all God's people gathered in peace and thankfulness universally.*

▶ Give this one a steady rhythm.

*Response: All*

Let us go to God's house to-day, let us go to God's house.

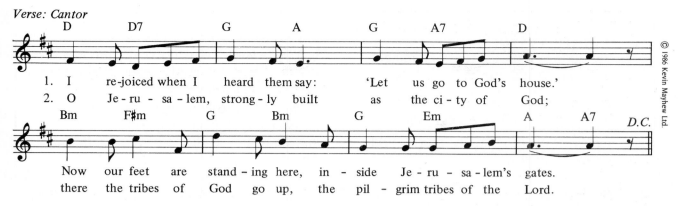

3. Just as Israel's law decrees
   there we praise the Lord's name,
   there are set the judgement thrones,
   where royal David is King.

4. Pray for peace in Jerusalem:
   'Peace to all whom you love;
   peace be here within your walls,
   and in your palaces, peace!'

## 27 ORDINARY TIME 10: Psalm 22
**Versified by Luke Connaughton
and Kevin Mayhew
Music by Kevin Mayhew**

*The loving shepherd cares for his flock, and he provides abundantly for all who belong to him – this image stirs the imagination of every generation, and has assured so many people of God's unfailing love.*

▶ Sing with confidence to reflect the text.

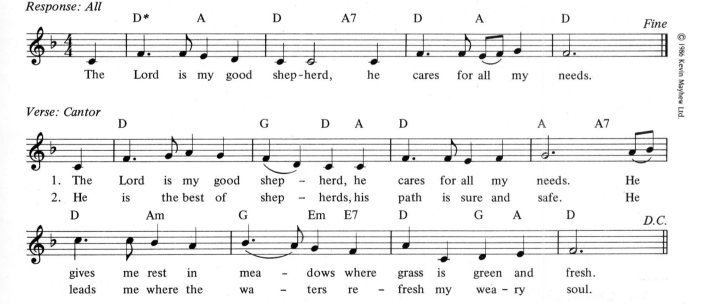

3. I will not fear the darkness
   for you are at my side.
   Your arm is there to lean on,
   your gentle strength is mine.

4. You let me feast in safety
   while all my foes looked on.
   You gave me rank and honour,
   I could not wish for more.

5. Your kindness will not leave me
   as long as life shall last.
   I live for ever, sharing
   God's holy house with him.

6. All praise to God the Father,
   all glory to the Son;
   and to the Holy Spirit
   a hymn of endless praise.

*\* Guitar Capo 3 if playing with keyboard.*

GOSPEL ACCLAMATION

As the Book of the Gospels, containing the Good News brought to us by Jesus, is carried in solemn procession to the lectern to be proclaimed, the Gospel Acclamation is sung. This ranks with the Sanctus and Great Amen in the trinity of acclamations that should always be sung at Mass.

The Cantor sings out the Response which is repeated enthusiastically by everyone present. This is followed by a short verse and everyone sings the Response again.

The Response alone may also be repeated immediately after the Gospel in place of the spoken response 'Praise to you, Lord Jesus Christ'.

## 28 ADVENT
### Music by Gerry Fitzpatrick

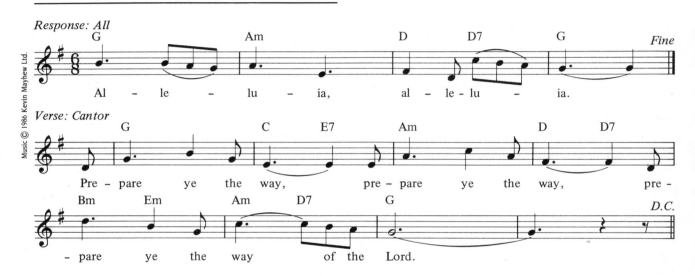

*Response: All*

Al - le - lu - ia, al - le - lu - ia.

*Verse: Cantor*

Pre - pare ye the way, pre - pare ye the way, pre - pare ye the way of the Lord.

## 29 CHRISTMAS
### Music by Gerry Fitzpatrick

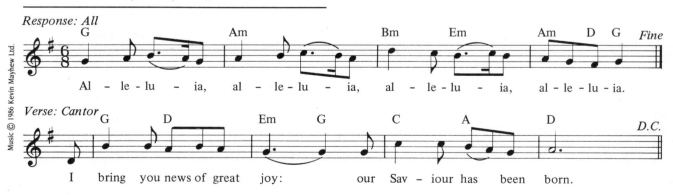

*Response: All*

Al - le - lu - ia, al - le - lu - ia, al - le - lu - ia, al - le - lu - ia.

*Verse: Cantor*

I bring you news of great joy: our Sav - iour has been born.

## 30 LENT
### Music by Kevin Mayhew

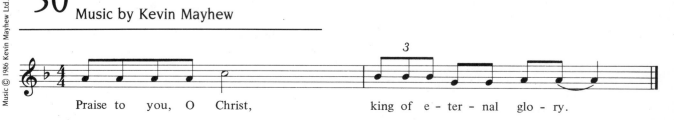

Praise to you, O Christ, king of e - ter - nal glo - ry.

## 31 LENT 2
Music by Gerry Fitzpatrick

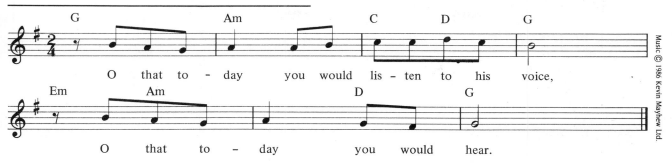

O that to - day you would lis - ten to his voice,

O that to - day you would hear.

## 32 LENT 3
Music by Gerry Fitzpatrick

Lord and Mas - ter, you are our way to God. Je - sus, Sav - iour, you

are the truth and life.

## 33 EASTER
Music by Gerry Fitzpatrick

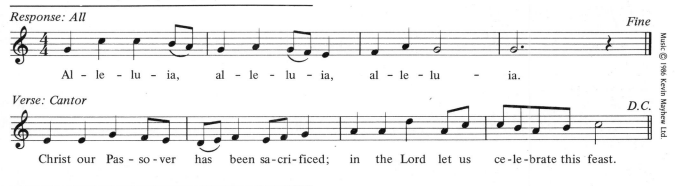

*Response: All*  *Fine*

Al - le - lu - ia, al - le - lu - ia, al - le - lu - ia.

*Verse: Cantor*  *D.C.*

Christ our Pas - so - ver has been sa - cri - ficed; in the Lord let us ce - le - brate this feast.

## 34 PENTECOST
Music by Gerry Fitzpatrick

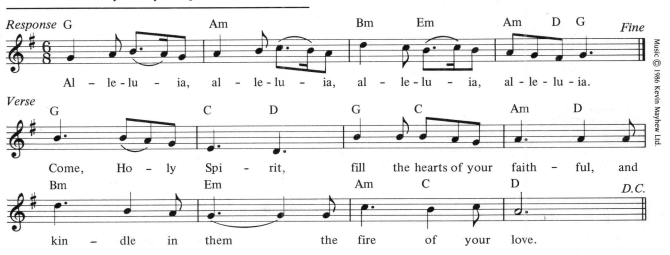

*Response*  *Fine*

Al - le - lu - ia, al - le - lu - ia, al - le - lu - ia, al - le - lu - ia.

*Verse*

Come, Ho - ly Spi - rit, fill the hearts of your faith - ful, and

kin - dle in them the fire of your love.  *D.C.*

## 35 ORDINARY TIME 1
Music by Gerry Fitzpatrick

Al - le - lu - ia, al - le - lu - ia, al - le - lu - ia.

## 36 ORDINARY TIME 2
Music by Kevin Mayhew

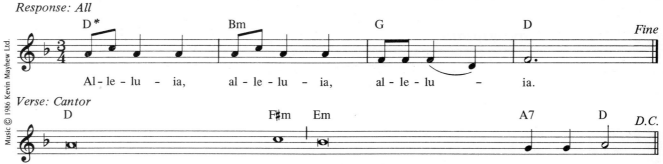

*Response: All*

Al - le - lu - ia, al - le - lu - ia, al - le - lu - ia.

*Verse: Cantor*

I am the light of the world, says the Lord, anyone who follows me will have the light of life.

*\*Guitar Capo 3 if playing with the keyboard.*

## 37 ORDINARY TIME 3
Music by Gerry Fitzpatrick

*Response: All*

Al - le - lu - ia, al - le - lu - ia, al - le - lu - ia.

*Verse: Cantor*

Speak, O Lord, your ser - vant is list' - ning, al - le - lu - ia.

## 38 ORDINARY TIME 4
Response: Plainsong
Verse: Music by Gerry Fitzpatrick

*Response: All*

Al - le - lu - ia, al - le - lu - ia, al - le - lu - ia.

*Verse: Cantor*

We hear the Word and God still speaks; Christ is the Word: we turn to him.

## 39 ORDINARY TIME 5
Words and Music
by Kevin Mayhew

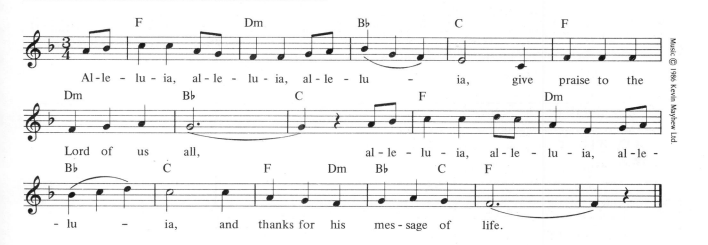

Al-le-lu-ia, al-le-lu-ia, al-le-lu - ia, give praise to the Lord of us all, al-le-lu-ia, al-le-lu-ia, al-le- -lu - ia, and thanks for his mes-sage of life.

## 40 RESPONSE TO THE READINGS
Music by Gerry Fitzpatrick

*Celebrant*     *All*

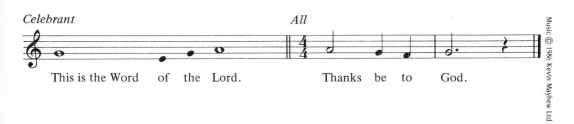

This is the Word of the Lord. Thanks be to God.

## 41 RESPONSE TO THE GOSPEL
Music by Gerry Fitzpatrick

*Celebrant*     *All*

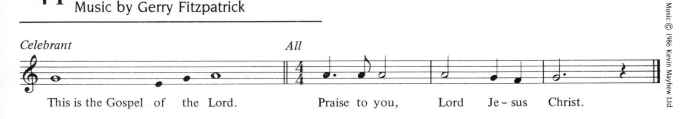

This is the Gospel of the Lord. Praise to you, Lord Je-sus Christ.

THE CREED

The Creed is a concise and convenient formula of the most important Christian beliefs. It was introduced into the Mass in the Eastern Church in the 5th century and spread to the rest of the Church. Through it we declare what we believe not just as isolated individuals but as members of the people of God, the community of the Church.

The text used in this setting is that provided for the Renewal of Baptismal Promises at the Easter Vigil.

# 42 THE CREED
## Music by Gerry Fitzpatrick

▶ The Celebrant will need to sing out with confidence so that the people pick up his mood for their Response.

*Celebrant*

Do you believe in God, the Father almighty, creator of heav'n and earth?

*All*

We be-lieve, we do be-lieve.

*Celebrant*

Do you believe in Jesus Christ, his only Son, our Lord, who was born of the Virgin Mary, was crucified, died and was buried?

*All*

We be-lieve, we do be-lieve.

*Celebrant*

Do you believe in Jesus Christ, who rose from the dead, and is now seated at the right hand of the Father?

*All*

We be-lieve, we do be-lieve.

*Celebrant*

Do you believe in the Holy Spirit, the holy Catholic Church, the com-munion of Saints?

*All*

We be-lieve, we do be-lieve.

**Celebrant**

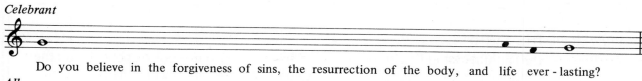

Do you believe in the forgiveness of sins, the resurrection of the body, and life ever - lasting?

*All*

We be -lieve, we do be -lieve.

PRAYER OF THE FAITHFUL

The Prayer of the Faithful (or Bidding Prayers) in one form or another is as old as the Church herself. In 1 Timothy 2:1-3 we find this passage 'My advice is that, first of all, there should be prayers offered for everyone – petitions, intercessions and thanksgiving – and especially for kings and others in authority, so that we may be able to live religious and reverent lives in peace and quiet.'

These are outward-looking petitions for the Church and the world which help the local community to see itself as part of the Christian and human family. Intercessions are made for the Church, for civil authorities, for the salvation of the world, for those who suffer and for the local community.

## RESPONSES TO THE BIDDING PRAYERS
Music by Kevin Mayhew

## 43 ADVENT

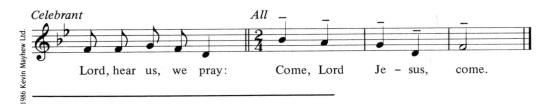

Lord, hear us, we pray: Come, Lord Je-sus, come.

## 44 CHRISTMAS

Lord, hear us: through the Word made flesh.

## 45 LENT

Lord, have mer-cy: and give us your sav-ing grace.

## 46 EASTER 1

Hear us, O Lord: in the name of the ri-sen Christ.

## 47 EASTER 2

Hear us, O Lord: al – le – lu – ia.

Music © 1986 Kevin Mayhew Ltd.

## 48 ORDINARY TIME 1

Lord, hear us: Lord, gra-cious-ly hear us.

## 49 ORDINARY TIME 2

We pray to you, Lord: may your king-dom come.

## 50 ORDINARY TIME 3

Lord, have mer-cy: and de – li – ver us from e – vil.

# Liturgy of the Eucharist

### SANCTUS

This acclamation, which forms the climax of the Preface, originates in the worship of the synagogue (Isaiah 6:3; Psalm 118:26). It is one of the great acclamations which should be sung if at all possible. It is the assembly's means of taking to itself the theme of praise and thanksgiving which is the Eucharistic Prayer. In the Sanctus we join the whole company of heaven in praising our loving Father.

## 51 SANCTUS 1
### Music by Patrick Appleford

▶ Start softly and build towards the 'Hosanna'. Soft again for 'Blessed is he', getting louder to the end.

## 52 SANCTUS 2
### Music by Noel Donnelly

▶ To be sung unaccompanied; best with the Cantor singing each phrase first.

Music © Kevin Mayhew Ltd.

Music © 1986 Kevin Mayhew Ltd.

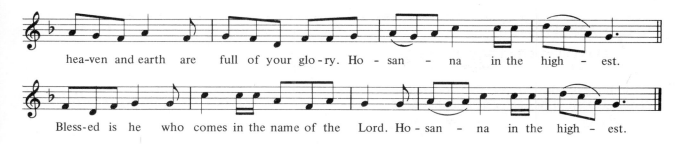

hea-ven and earth are full of your glo-ry. Ho-san-na in the high-est.

Bless-ed is he who comes in the name of the Lord. Ho-san-na in the high-est.

## 53 SANCTUS 3
### Music: Composer unknown

▸ Take this gently: it has a deeply prayerful feel to it; build towards the end.

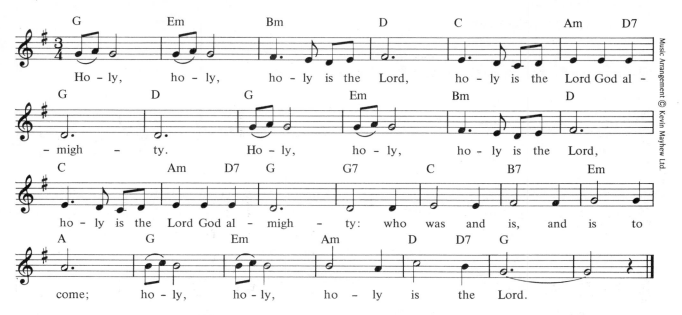

Ho-ly, ho-ly, ho-ly is the Lord, ho-ly is the Lord God al-migh-ty. Ho-ly, ho-ly, ho-ly is the Lord, ho-ly is the Lord God al-migh-ty: who was and is, and is to come; ho-ly, ho-ly, ho-ly is the Lord.

Music Arrangement © Kevin Mayhew Ltd.

## 54 SANCTUS 4
### Music by Clare Lee

▸ A truly happy setting! Sing it with enjoyment.

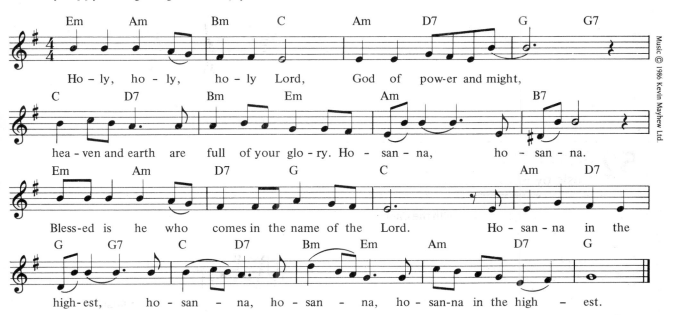

Ho-ly, ho-ly, ho-ly Lord, God of pow-er and might, hea-ven and earth are full of your glo-ry. Ho-san-na, ho-san-na. Bless-ed is he who comes in the name of the Lord. Ho-san-na in the high-est, ho-san-na, ho-san-na, ho-san-na in the high-est.

Music © 1986 Kevin Mayhew Ltd.

## 55 SANCTUS 5
### Music by Gerry Fitzpatrick

▶ Try to bring out the 'Scottish' flavour of this
setting. The use of the Cantor in the middle adds
interest.

Music © Kevin Mayhew Ltd.

**All**
Ho - ly, ho - ly, ho - ly Lord, God of power and might,
hea-ven and earth are full of your glo - ry. Ho - san - na in the
high - est, ho - san - na in the high - est.

**Cantor**
Bless - ed is he:

**All**
bless - ed is he

**Cantor**
who comes in the name of the Lord:

**All**
who comes in the name of the Lord.

Ho - san - na in the high - est, ho -
- san - na in the high - est.

MEMORIAL ACCLAMATION
Following immediately on the Consecration, the Memorial Acclamation is the means by which the people profess their faith in the mystery of salvation: achieved by Christ, it is given to us today and we await its full realisation.

## 56 MEMORIAL ACCLAMATION 1
Music by Kevin Mayhew

▶ Reminder! It makes it easier for the people if the Cantor sings each phrase first.

*Celebrant*

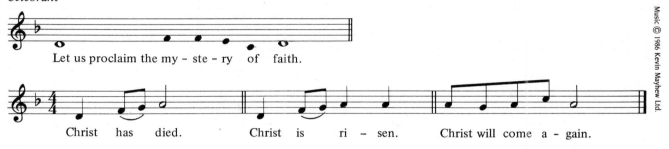

## 57 MEMORIAL ACCLAMATION 2
Music by Noel Donnelly

*Celebrant*

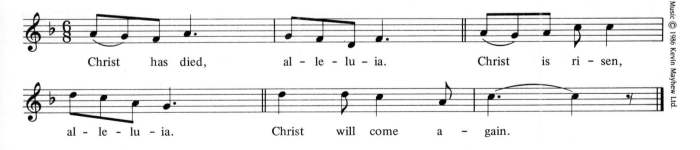

## 58 MEMORIAL ACCLAMATION 3
Music by Kevin Mayhew

*Celebrant*

## 59 MEMORIAL ACCLAMATION 4
### Music by Estelle White

*Celebrant*

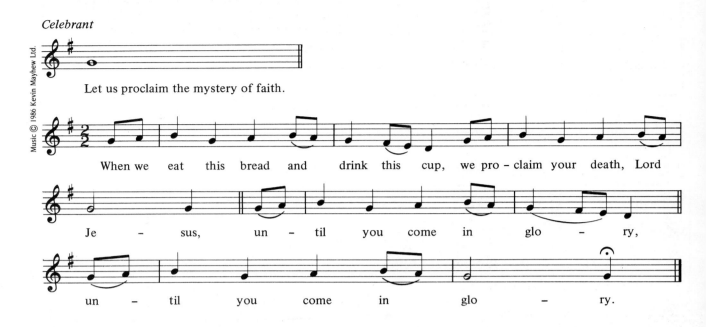

Let us proclaim the mystery of faith.

When we eat this bread and drink this cup, we pro-claim your death, Lord Je-sus, un-til you come in glo-ry, un-til you come in glo-ry.

## 60 MEMORIAL ACCLAMATION 5
### Music by Estelle White

*Celebrant*

Let us proclaim the mystery of faith.

Lord, by your cross and re-sur-rec-tion, you have set us free. You are the Sa-viour of the world.

Music © 1986 Kevin Mayhew Ltd.

**GREAT AMEN**

The great doxology (a Greek word indicating the giving of praise in its highest form to the Father, through, with and in Jesus Christ, in the unity of the Holy Spirit) ends with the Great Amen. By our enthusiastic 'Amen' we make the prayer our own. It is our 'yes' to all that has been said in the Eucharistic Prayer, our assent as believers in a Christian community to all that has taken place in our presence and in our name.

## 61 GREAT AMEN 1
Music by Kevin Mayhew

▶ Reminder! It makes it easier for the people if the Cantor sings each phrase first.

*Celebrant*

Through him........ ever and ev - er.

A - men, a - men.

## 62 GREAT AMEN 2
Music by Kevin Mayhew

*Celebrant*

Through him........ ever and ev - er.

A - men, a - men, a - men.

## 63 GREAT AMEN 3
Music by Noel Donnelly

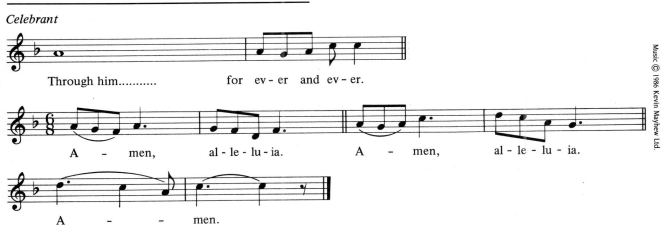

*Celebrant*

Through him.......... for ev - er and ev - er.

A - men, al - le - lu - ia. A - men, al - le - lu - ia.

A - men.

## 64 GREAT AMEN 4
### Music by Kevin Mayhew

# Communion Rite

THE LORD'S PRAYER
and DOXOLOGY

This is the prayer that Jesus himself taught us (*Matthew* 6:9). 'Pray like this', he said. It is a petition for daily food which for Christians means the eucharistic bread, and for forgiveness of sin, so that what is holy may be given to those who are holy.

After the Lord's Prayer the celebrant continues with the prayer 'Deliver us, Lord, from every evil'. This is called the embolism, (a Greek word meaning 'stopgap', a prayer 'thrust in' between the Lord's Prayer and the Breaking of Bread). It develops the last petition of the Lord's Prayer and begs, in the name of the community, deliverance from the power of evil.

Everyone assents with a final acclamation.

## 65 THE LORD'S PRAYER 1
### Music by Julian Wiener

▶ Keep this one moving, but not too much.

Our Fa - ther, who art in hea - ven, hal-lowed be thy name; thy king-dom come, thy will be done on earth as it is in hea - ven. Give us this day our dai-ly bread, and for-give us our tres-pas - ses as we for - give those who tres-pass a - gainst us and lead us not in - to temp-ta - tion, but de-li - ver us from all that is e - vil.

*Continue playing:* |D |Bm |G |A | *under the prayer.*

*Doxology* For the king - dom, the power and the glo - ry are yours now and for ev-er. A - men.

# 66 THE LORD'S PRAYER 2
Music by Patrick Appleford

▶ Gently and prayerfully.

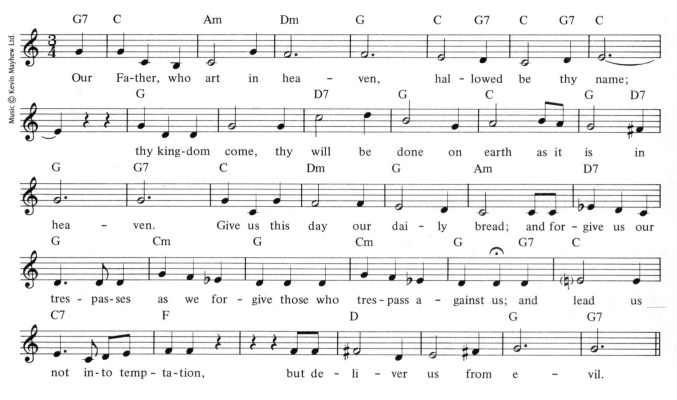

Our Fa-ther, who art in hea - ven, hal - lowed be thy name;
thy king-dom come, thy will be done on earth as it is in
hea - ven. Give us this day our dai - ly bread; and for - give us our
tres - pas-ses as we for - give those who tres-pass a - gainst us; and lead us
not in-to temp - ta-tion, but de - li - ver us from e - vil.

*Continue playing:* |Dm |Dm |G |G |*under the prayer.*

*Doxology*

For the king-dom, the power, and the glo-ry are yours, now
and for ev - er. A - men.

LAMB OF GOD

These are the words of John the Baptist when he saw Jesus approaching: 'Look, the Lamb of God, who takes away the sin of the world' (John 1:29). They are sung during the Breaking of Bread and may be repeated as often as necessary to accompany this (not just three times). The singing is brought to a close by the words 'grant us peace'.

## 67 LAMB OF GOD 1
### Music by Gerry Fitzpatrick

▶ Not too fast and fairly smoothly.

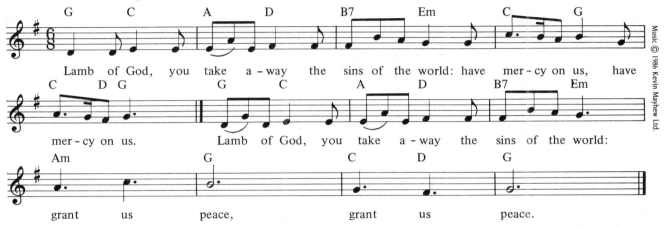

## 68 LAMB OF GOD 2
### Music by Kevin Mayhew

▶ To be sung unaccompanied in a fairly robust manner.

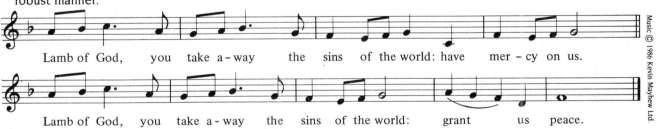

## 69 LAMB OF GOD 3
### Music by Estelle White

▶ Gently and quietly.

## 70 LAMB OF GOD 4
Music by Kevin Mayhew

▶ Another unaccompanied setting to be sung like a chant.

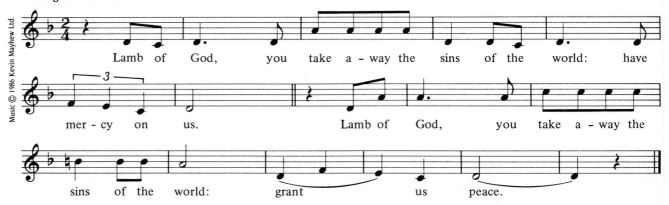

Lamb of God, you take a - way the sins of the world: have mer - cy on us. Lamb of God, you take a - way the sins of the world: grant us peace.

## 71 THE DISMISSAL
Music by Kevin Mayhew

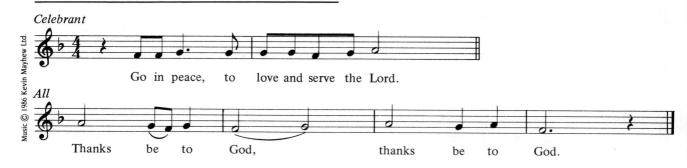

*Celebrant*

Go in peace, to love and serve the Lord.

*All*

Thanks be to God, thanks be to God.

# RESPONSORIAL PSALM INDEX

*In this index a psalm is suggested for each Sunday and major feast of the three-year cycle of Readings. The choice is based on careful study of the Lectionary and attempts to reflect the theme of the day.*

## ADVENT

### 1st Sunday
| | | |
|---|---|---|
| Year A | Psalm 121 | 26 |
| | Psalm 84 | 10 |
| Year B | Psalm 94 | 22 |
| | Psalm 24 | 9 |
| Year C | Psalm 24 | 9 |

### 2nd Sunday
| | | |
|---|---|---|
| Year A | Psalm 84 | 10 |
| Year B | Psalm 84 | 10 |
| Year C | Psalm 84 | 10 |

### 3rd Sunday
| | | |
|---|---|---|
| Year A | Psalm 24 | 9 |
| | Psalm 103 | 17 |
| Year B | Psalm 84 | 10 |
| | Psalm 26 | 19 |
| Year C | Psalm 65 | 16 |
| | Psalm 84 | 10 |

### 4th Sunday
| | | |
|---|---|---|
| Year A | Psalm 24 | 9 |
| | Psalm 144 | 25 |
| Year B | Psalm 84 | 10 |
| | Psalm 18 | 18 |
| Year C | Psalm 24 | 9 |
| | Psalm 103 | 17 |

## CHRISTMAS MIDNIGHT
| | | |
|---|---|---|
| Year A | Psalm 97 | 11 |
| Year B | Psalm 97 | 11 |
| Year C | Psalm 97 | 11 |

## CHRISTMAS DAWN
| | | |
|---|---|---|
| Year A | Psalm 97 | 11 |
| | Psalm 144 | 25 |
| Year B | Psalm 97 | 11 |
| | Psalm 144 | 25 |
| Year C | Psalm 97 | 11 |
| | Psalm 144 | 25 |

## CHRISTMAS DAY
| | | |
|---|---|---|
| Year A | Psalm 97 | 11 |
| Year B | Psalm 97 | 11 |
| Year C | Psalm 97 | 11 |

## THE HOLY FAMILY
| | | |
|---|---|---|
| Year A | Psalm 18 | 18 |
| Year B | Psalm 97 | 11 |
| Year C | Psalm 26 | 19 |

## MARY, MOTHER OF GOD
| | | |
|---|---|---|
| Year A | Psalm 102 | 24 |
| Year B | Psalm 102 | 24 |
| Year C | Psalm 102 | 24 |

## 2nd SUNDAY OF CHRISTMAS
| | | |
|---|---|---|
| Year A | Psalm 97 | 11 |
| | Psalm 65 | 16 |
| Year B | Psalm 97 | 11 |
| | Psalm 65 | 16 |
| Year C | Psalm 97 | 11 |
| | Psalm 65 | 16 |

## EPIPHANY
| | | |
|---|---|---|
| Years A, B, C | Psalm 97 | 11 |

## BAPTISM OF THE LORD
| | | |
|---|---|---|
| Year A | Psalm 144 | 25 |
| Year B | Psalm 102 | 24 |
| Year C | Psalm 103 | 17 |

## LENT

### Ash Wednesday
| | | |
|---|---|---|
| Year A | Psalm 50 | 12 |
| Year B | Psalm 50 | 12 |
| Year C | Psalm 50 | 12 |
| | Psalm 103 | 17 |

### 1st Sunday of Lent
| | | |
|---|---|---|
| Year A | Psalm 50 | 12 |
| Year B | Psalm 24 | 9 |
| Year C | Psalm 90 | 14 |

### 2nd Sunday of Lent
| | | |
|---|---|---|
| Year A | Psalm 18 | 18 |
| Year B | Psalm 26 | 19 |
| Year C | Psalm 26 | 19 |

### 3rd Sunday of Lent
| | | |
|---|---|---|
| Year A | Psalm 94 | 22 |
| Year B | Psalm 18 | 18 |
| Year C | Psalm 102 | 24 |

### 4th Sunday of Lent
| | | |
|---|---|---|
| Year A | Psalm 22 | 27 |
| Year B | Psalm 94 | 22 |
| Year C | Psalm 33 | 26 |

### 5th Sunday of Lent
| | | |
|---|---|---|
| Year A | Psalm 129 | 14 |
| Year B | Psalm 50 | 12 |
| Year C | Psalm 62 | 21 |

## HOLY WEEK
(See *Focus on Holy Week*)

### Passion (Palm) Sunday
| | | |
|---|---|---|
| Years A, B, C | Psalm 50 | 12 |

### Holy Thursday
| | | |
|---|---|---|
| Year A | Psalm 26 | 19 |
| | Psalm 62 | 21 |
| Year B | Psalm 26 | 19 |
| | Psalm 62 | 21 |
| Year C | Psalm 26 | 19 |
| | Psalm 62 | 21 |

### Good Friday
| | | |
|---|---|---|
| Years A, B, C | Psalm 50 | 12 |

## THE EASTER VIGIL
| | | |
|---|---|---|
| Year A | Psalm 103 | 17 |
| | Psalm 18 | 18 |
| Year B | Psalm 103 | 17 |
| | Psalm 18 | 18 |
| Year C | Psalm 103 | 17 |
| | Psalm 18 | 18 |

### Easter Sunday
| | | |
|---|---|---|
| Year A | Psalm 117 | 15 |
| Year B | Psalm 117 | 15 |
| Year C | Psalm 117 | 15 |

### 2nd Sunday of Easter
| | | |
|---|---|---|
| Year A | Psalm 117 | 15 |
| Year B | Psalm 117 | 15 |
| Year C | Psalm 117 | 15 |

### 3rd Sunday of Easter
| | | |
|---|---|---|
| Year A | Psalm 144 | 25 |
| Year B | Psalm 102 | 24 |
| Year C | Psalm 33 | 20 |

### 4th Sunday of Easter
| | | |
|---|---|---|
| Year A | Psalm 22 | 27 |
| Year B | Psalm 117 | 15 |
| Year C | Psalm 99 | 23 |

### 5th Sunday of Easter
| | | |
|---|---|---|
| Year A | Psalm 65 | 16 |
| Year B | Psalm 97 | 11 |
| Year C | Psalm 144 | 25 |

### 6th Sunday of Easter
| | | |
|---|---|---|
| Year A | Psalm 65 | 16 |
| Year B | Psalm 97 | 11 |
| Year C | Psalm 18 | 18 |

### Ascension
| | | |
|---|---|---|
| Years A, B, C | Psalm 65 | 16 |

### 7th Sunday of Easter
| | | |
|---|---|---|
| Year A | Psalm 26 | 19 |
| Year B | Psalm 102 | 24 |
| Year C | Psalm 99 | 23 |

### Pentecost
| | | |
|---|---|---|
| Year A | Psalm 103 | 17 |
| Year B | Psalm 103 | 17 |
| Year C | Psalm 103 | 17 |

### The Most Holy Trinity
| | | |
|---|---|---|
| Year A | Psalm 144 | 25 |
| Year B | Psalm 144 | 25 |
| | Psalm 18 | 18 |
| Year C | Psalm 103 | 17 |

## ORDINARY TIME

### 1st Sunday
(Baptism of the Lord)
| | | |
|---|---|---|
| Year A | Psalm 90 | 13 |
| Year B | Psalm 90 | 13 |
| | Psalm 65 | 16 |
| Year C | Psalm 103 | 17 |

### 2nd Sunday
| | | |
|---|---|---|
| Year A | Psalm 26 | 19 |
| | Psalm 65 | 16 |
| Year B | Psalm 33 | 20 |
| | Psalm 99 | 23 |
| Year C | Psalm 18 | 18 |
| | Psalm 94 | 22 |

### 3rd Sunday
| | | |
|---|---|---|
| Year A | Psalm 26 | 19 |
| Year B | Psalm 24 | 9 |
| Year C | Psalm 18 | 18 |

**4th Sunday**

| Year A | Psalm 33 | 20 |
| | Psalm 144 | 25 |
| Year B | Psalm 94 | 22 |
| Year C | Psalm 26 | 19 |
| | Psalm 102 | 24 |

**5th Sunday**

| Year A | Psalm 26 | 19 |
| Year B | Psalm 22 | 27 |
| | Psalm 102 | 24 |
| Year C | Psalm 144 | 25 |
| | Psalm 102 | 24 |

**6th Sunday**

| Year A | Psalm 18 | 18 |
| Year B | Psalm 103 | 17 |
| | Psalm 102 | 24 |
| Year C | Psalm 26 | 19 |
| | Psalm 22 | 27 |

**7th Sunday**

| Year A | Psalm 102 | 24 |
| Year B | Psalm 129 | 14 |
| Year C | Psalm 102 | 24 |

**8th Sunday**

| Year A | Psalm 26 | 19 |
| | Psalm 90 | 13 |
| Year B | Psalm 102 | 24 |
| Year C | Psalm 117 | 15 |
| | Psalm 18 | 18 |

**9th Sunday**

| Year A | Psalm 90 | 13 |
| | Psalm 18 | 18 |
| Year B | Psalm 33 | 20 |
| | Psalm 18 | 18 |
| Year C | Psalm 97 | 11 |

**10th Sunday**

| Year A | Psalm 94 | 22 |
| | Psalm 121 | 26 |
| Year B | Psalm 129 | 14 |
| Year C | Psalm 33 | 20 |

**11th Sunday**

| Year A | Psalm 99 | 23 |
| Year B | Psalm 97 | 11 |
| Year C | Psalm 50 | 12 |

**12th Sunday**

| Year A | Psalm 129 | 14 |
| | Psalm 62 | 21 |
| Year B | Psalm 65 | 16 |
| | Psalm 99 | 23 |
| Year C | Psalm 62 | 21 |

**13th Sunday**

| Year A | Psalm 144 | 25 |
| Year B | Psalm 117 | 15 |
| | Psalm 22 | 27 |
| Year C | Psalm 24 | 9 |

**14th Sunday**

| Year A | Psalm 144 | 25 |
| Year B | Psalm 94 | 22 |
| Year C | Psalm 65 | 16 |

**15th Sunday**

| Year A | Psalm 103 | 17 |
| Year B | Psalm 84 | 10 |
| Year C | Psalm 18 | 18 |

**16th Sunday**

| Year A | Psalm 129 | 14 |
| Year B | Psalm 22 | 27 |
| Year C | Psalm 90 | 13 |
| | Psalm 62 | 21 |

**17th Sunday**

| Years A | Psalm 18 | 18 |
| Year B | Psalm 144 | 25 |
| Year C | Psalm 33 | 20 |

**18th Sunday**

| Year A | Psalm 144 | 25 |
| Year B | Psalm 33 | 20 |
| | Psalm 18 | 18 |
| Year C | Psalm 94 | 22 |

**19th Sunday**

| Year A | Psalm 84 | 10 |
| Year B | Psalm 33 | 20 |
| Year C | Psalm 94 | 22 |

**20th Sunday**

| Year A | Psalm 65 | 16 |
| Year B | Psalm 33 | 20 |
| Year C | Psalm 129 | 14 |
| | Psalm 90 | 13 |

**21st Sunday**

| Year A | Psalm 144 | 25 |
| | Psalm 62 | 21 |
| Year B | Psalm 33 | 20 |
| Year C | Psalm 65 | 16 |

**22nd Sunday**

| Year A | Psalm 62 | 21 |
| Year B | Psalm 18 | 18 |
| | Psalm 94 | 22 |
| Year C | Psalm 22 | 27 |

**23rd Sunday**

| Year A | Psalm 94 | 22 |
| Year B | Psalm 144 | 25 |
| Year C | Psalm 26 | 19 |
| | Psalm 103 | 17 |

**24th Sunday**

| Year A | Psalm 102 | 24 |
| Year B | Psalm 117 | 15 |
| | Psalm 129 | 14 |
| Year C | Psalm 50 | 12 |

**25th Sunday**

| Year A | Psalm 144 | 25 |
| Year B | Psalm 24 | 9 |
| | Psalm 26 | 19 |
| Year C | Psalm 65 | 16 |

**26th Sunday**

| Year A | Psalm 24 | 9 |
| Year B | Psalm 18 | 18 |
| Year C | Psalm 103 | 17 |

**27th Sunday**

| Year A | Psalm 117 | 15 |
| | Psalm 129 | 14 |
| Year B | Psalm 99 | 23 |
| | Psalm 121 | 26 |
| Year C | Psalm 94 | 22 |

**28th Sunday**

| Year A | Psalm 22 | 27 |
| Year B | Psalm 62 | 21 |
| Year C | Psalm 97 | 11 |

**29th Sunday**

| Year A | Psalm 65 | 16 |
| Year B | Psalm 84 | 10 |
| | Psalm 90 | 13 |
| Year C | Psalm 22 | 27 |
| | Psalm 90 | 13 |

**30th Sunday**

| Year A | Psalm 18 | 18 |
| | Psalm 24 | 9 |
| Year B | Psalm 65 | 16 |
| | Psalm 144 | 25 |
| Year C | Psalm 33 | 20 |

**31st Sunday**

| Year A | Psalm 33 | 20 |
| Year B | Psalm 26 | 19 |
| Year C | Psalm 144 | 25 |

**32nd Sunday**

| Year A | Psalm 62 | 21 |
| Year B | Psalm 94 | 22 |
| | Psalm 103 | 17 |
| Year C | Psalm 62 | 21 |

**33rd Sunday**

| Year A | Psalm 94 | 22 |
| | Psalm 121 | 26 |
| Year B | Psalm 26 | 19 |
| | Psalm 129 | 14 |
| Year C | Psalm 97 | 11 |

**Last Sunday in Ordinary Time (Our Lord Jesus Christ, Universal King)**

| Year A | Psalm 22 | 27 |
| Year B | Psalm 144 | 25 |
| Year C | Psalm 121 | 26 |